WHY IS THE SKY?

# Why Is the Sky?

*edited by* John Agard

*with illustrations by* Andrzej Klimowski

faber and faber
LONDON · BOSTON

First published in 1996
by Faber and Faber Limited
3 Queen Square London WC1N 3AU

Photoset by Wilmaset Ltd, Wirral
Printed in England by Clays Ltd, St Ives plc

John Agard is hereby identified as the editor of this
work in accordance with Section 77 of the Copyright,
Designs and Patents Act 1988

A CIP record for this book
is available from the British Library

ISBN 0–571–17686–0

10 9 8 7 6 5 4 3 2 1

MONK: 'All these mountains and rivers and the great earth — where do they come from?'

MASTER: 'Where does this question of yours come from?'

*The World of Zen*

# Contents

# Questions at Night

Why
Is the sky?

What starts the thunder overhead?
Who makes the crashing noise?
Are the angels falling out of bed?
Are they breaking all their toys?

Why does the sun go down so soon?
Why do the night-clouds crawl
Hungrily up to the new-laid moon
And swallow it, shell and all?

If there's a Bear among the stars,
As all the people say,
Won't he jump over those pasture-bars
And drink up the Milky Way?

Does every star that happens to fall
Turn into a firefly?
Can't it ever get back to Heaven at all?
And why
Is the sky?

LOUIS UNTERMEYER (1885–1978), USA

# How Many Stars?

When I was a boy
I would ask my dad:
'How many stars are there hanging in the sky?'
'More than enough, son,
More than I could say.
Enough to keep you counting
Till your dying day.'

When I was a boy
I would ask my dad:
'How many fishes are there swimming in the sea?'
'More than enough, son,
More than I could say.
Enough to keep you counting
Till your dying day.'

When I was a boy
I would ask my dad:
'How many creepy-crawlies are there in the world?'
'More than enough, son.
More than I could say.
Enough to keep you counting
Till your dying day.'

It seemed like there wasn't anything my dad didn't
    know.

COLIN MCNAUGHTON, UK

2

# A New Hymn to the Sun

Sun,
what did you do
with the dark?
chase her away?
do her in
and devour her?

Or did you embrace
and hide her away
in your arms of light?

Is the dark your enemy,
something you eat?
or love maybe:
did she get so dark
not knowing where you were
all night?

And when you arrived,
did she lose herself
in you, your light?

Maybe your brother
and sister,
and your mother
asked you both
to take turns
watching over the world.

Don't you die,
are you immortals?
I praise you both,

and especially you,
O Sun.

SUBRAMANYA BHARATI (1882–1921), India

# Who Will Stop the Sun?

The sun walks about the sky, so
why shouldn't I walk about here below?

Why shouldn't I walk about like the sun?
Why should I only walk? I will run!

Who will listen to what I say, as I
wander about crying alone in this

large village? My heart will run
backwards, lamenting. Who will stop me

from getting what I want? Who will
stop the sun when he starts out walking?

Why does my heart feel so small
and speak with such a small voice?

I am small too. But who will
stop me from having my own way?

NATIVE AMERICAN: TSIMSHIAN
adapted by Brian Swann

# How?

How did the sun get up in the sky?
– A billy goat tossed it up too high,
Said my Uncle.

How did the stars get up there too?
– They're sparks from the thunder-horse's shoe,
Said my Uncle.

And tell me about the moon as well.
– The moon jumped out of an oyster shell,
Said my Uncle.

And how did the oceans get so deep?
– I'll tell you tomorrow. Now go to sleep,
Said my Uncle.

RICHARD EDWARDS, UK

# Water, Where Are You Going?

Water, where are you going?

  I am going down the river, gurgling
to the shores of the sea.

  Ocean, where are you going?

  Up the river I go looking
for the source where I can lie at ease.

  Poplar, and you? What will you do?

  I don't want to tell you . . .
nothing. Trembling . . . I will be!

  What do I want, what don't I want,
by the river and by the sea?

  (Four birds without direction
are high in the poplar tree.)

FEDERIGO GARCÍA LORCA (1899–1936), Spain
translated by Will Kirkland

# Thoughts like an Ocean

The sea comes to me on the shore
On lacy slippered feet
And shyly, slyly slides away
With a murmur of defeat.

And as I stand there wondering
Strange thoughts spin round my head
Of why and where and what and when
And if not, why, what then?

Where do lobsters come from?
And where anemones?
And are there other worlds out there
With other mysteries?

Why do *I* walk upon dry land
While fishes haunt the sea?
And as I think about their lives
Do they too think of me?

Why is water, water?
Why does it wet my hand?
Are there really as many stars
As there are grains of sand?

And where would the ocean go to
If there were no gravity?
And where was I before I lived?
And where's eternity?

Perhaps the beach I'm standing on
Perhaps this stretch of sand
Perhaps the Universe itself
Lies on someone else's hand?

And isn't it strange how this water and I
At this moment happened to meet
And how this tide sweeps half the world
Before stopping at my feet.

GARETH OWEN, UK

# Morwenstow

Where do you come from, sea,
To the sharp Cornish shore,
Leaping up to the raven's crag?
   *From Labrador.*

Do you grow tired, sea?
Are you weary ever
When the storms burst over your head?
   *Never.*

Are you hard as a diamond, sea,
As iron, as oak?
Are you stronger than flint or steel?
   *And the lightning stroke.*

Ten thousand years and more, sea,
You have gobbled your fill,
Swallowing stone and slate!
   *I am hungry still.*

When will you rest, sea?
   *When moon and sun*
   *Ride only fields of salt water*
   *And the land is gone.*

CHARLES CAUSLEY, UK

# If all rivers are sweet

If all rivers are sweet
where does the sea get its salt?

How do the seasons know
they must change their shirt?

Why so slowly in winter
and later with such a rapid shudder?

And how do the roots know
they must climb toward the light?

And then greet the air
with so many flowers and colours?

Is it always the same spring
who revives her role?

PABLO NERUDA (1834–91), Chile
translated by William O'Daly

# Once the Wind

Once the wind
said to the sea
I am sad
        And the sea said
Why
        And the wind said
Because I
am not blue like the sky
or like you

        So the sea said what's
so sad about that
                Lots
of things are blue
or red or other colours too
        but nothing
neither sea nor sky
can blow so strong
or sing so long as you

        And the sea looked sad
          So the wind said
Why

SHAKE KEANE, St Vincent, Caribbean

# Waves

There are waves to chase and waves that crash,
There are waves to jump like skipping ropes,
Waves to run away to sand, waves to leap and bound.
Waves that are turquoise, waves that are brown,
Waves full of seaweed, waves that drown.
Waves clear and calm, waves angry and wronged,
Waves that whisper, waves that roar like thunder,
Waves you'd never swim under, pounding rocks and
    shore.
Waves that put you to sleep, sssh sssh sssh cradle-rock.
Waves that look like sea horses or sheep or curly froth.
Waves that are cold as bare floor, waves that are warm
    as toast.
There are waves called the Black Sea, the Red Sea, the
    North Sea,
Waves called the Pacific ocean, the Atlantic ocean, the
    Antarctic.
If you counted them all, wave upon wave upon wave
would it be a hundred, a thousand, a billion – or more?

JACKIE KAY, Nigeria/Scotland

## *from* The Bijak of Kabir

In the forest how many leaves?
In the Ganga how many grains?
The pandits racked their brains.
From Kabir's mouth one word came.

＊

Colour is born of colour.
I see all colours one.
What colour is a living creature?
Solve it if you can.

KABIR (1398–1448), India
translated by Linda Hess and Shukdev Fingh

# How Laughter Helped Stop the Argument

FIRST VOICE:
> Look at the clouds
> so fluffy
> so sheepy
> That's because God
> got woolly hair.

SECOND VOICE:
> Look at the rain
> falling strands
> falling everywhere
> That's because God
> got straight hair.

THIRD VOICE:
> Look at de sun
> look at de moon
> That's why
> God got a yellow eye.

FOURTH VOICE:
> Look at the sea
> look at the sky
> That's a clue
> God's skin must be blue.

FIFTH VOICE:
    What about the night
    that wraps us dark
    and makes us sleep tight?
    God's skin must be black.

SIXTH VOICE:
    What about the snow?
    Oh no, God's skin must be white.

THIRD VOICE:
    No, God's skin must be green
    look at de trees
    See what I mean.

FIRST VOICE:
    Well, then since you are all so clever
    just answer me
    Is God a father or a mother?

SECOND VOICE:
    A father.

FIFTH VOICE:
    A mother.

SIXTH VOICE:
    No, a father.

THIRD VOICE:
    How about a grandmother?

AND WHILE THESE SIX VOICES
WERE ARGUING AND ARGUING
JUST THEN A SEVENTH VOICE STEPPED IN

Listen my friends
and listen well
crick me your ears
and I'll crack you a spell

God might be a story
with no beginning
and no end

God might be laughter
for all you know
God might be a HA-HA-HA-HAaaaaaaaaaaaa
a HO-HO-HO-HOoooooooooooo
a HE-HE-HE-HEeeeeeeeeeeee
a SHE-SHE-SHE-SHEeeecceeeeeeee

a million million
laughing pebbles
inside of
you and me.

That's what God might be.

JOHN AGARD, Guyana/UK

17

# Questions, Quistions & Quoshtions

Daddy how does an elephant feel
When he swallows a piece of steel?
Does he get drunk
And fall on his trunk
Or roll down the road like a wheel?

Daddy what would a pelican do
If he swallowed a bottle of glue?
Would his beak get stuck
Would he run out of luck
And lose his job at the zoo?

Son tell me tell me true,
If I belted you with a shoe,
Would you fall down dead?
Would you go up to bed?
— Either of those would do.

SPIKE MILLIGAN, UK

# The Answers

'When did the world begin and how?'
I asked a lamb, a goat, a cow:

'What's it all about and why?'
I asked a hog as he went by:

'Where will the whole thing end, and when?'
I asked a duck, a goose, a hen:

And I copied all the answers too,
A quack, a honk, an oink, a moo.

ROBERT CLAIRMONT, UK

# The Joy of Fishes

Chuang Tzu and Hui Tzu
Were crossing Hao river
By the dam.

Chuang said:
'See how free
The fishes leap and dart:
That is their happiness.'

Hui replied:
'Since you are not a fish
How do you know
What makes fishes happy?'

Chuang said:
'Since you are not I
How can you possibly know
That I do not know
What makes fishes happy?'

Hui argued:
'If I, not being you,
Cannot know what you know
It follows that you
Not being a fish
Cannot know what they know.'

*from* The Way of Chuang Tzu (4th–3rd century BC), China
translated by Thomas Merton

# How Fly the Birds of Heaven

How fly the birds of heaven save by their wings?
How tread the stags, those huge and hairy things,
Save by their feet? How do the fishes turn
In their wet purlieus, where the mermaids yearn,
Save by their tails? How does the plantain sprout,
Save by that root it cannot do without,
I hope that I have made my meaning clear . . .

MERVYN PEAKE (1911–68), UK

# Zebra Question

I asked the zebra,
Are you black with white stripes?
Or white with black stripes?
And the zebra asked me,
Are you good with bad habits?
Or are you bad with good habits?
Are you noisy with quiet times?
Or are you quiet with noisy times?
Are you happy with some sad days?
Or are you sad with some happy days?
Are you neat with some sloppy ways?
Or are you sloppy with some neat ways?
And on and on and on and on
And on and on he went.
I'll never ask a zebra
About stripes
Again.

SHEL SILVERSTEIN, USA

# Bulls and Snails

Why can't bulls see with the ends of their horns
Like snails
Since they were created with horns?

Why don't snails butt with their horns?
Like bulls
Since they were born with horns?

Why don't bulls withdraw inside themselves
Like snails
When we caress their soft muzzles?

Why don't bulls leave a trace
Like snails
When enchanted they encounter the sun?

JON MILOS, Romania/Serbo-Croatia
translated by Brenda Walker

# The Tyger

Tyger! Tyger! burning bright
In the forests of the night
What immortal hand or eye
Could frame thy fearful symmetry?

In what distant deeps or skies
Burnt the fire of thine eyes?
On what wings dare he aspire?
What the hand dare seize the fire?

And what shoulder, & what art
Could twist the sinews of thy heart?
And when thy heart began to beat,
What dread hand? & what dread feet?

What the hammer? what the chain,
In what furnace was thy brain?
What the anvil? what dread grasp
Dare its deadly terrors clasp?

When the stars threw down their spears,
And water'd heaven with their tears,
Did he smile his work to see?
Did he who made the Lamb make thee?

Tyger! Tyger! burning bright
In the forests of the night,
What immortal hand or eye
Dare frame thy fearful symmetry?

WILLIAM BLAKE (1757–1827), UK

# Don't Cry Caterpillar

Don't cry, Caterpillar
Caterpillar, don't cry
You'll be a butterfly – by and by.

Caterpillar, please
Don't worry 'bout a thing

'But,' said Caterpillar,
'Will I still know myself – in wings?'

GRACE NICHOLS, Guyana/UK

## *from* What Is the Truth?

Why is it
The roustabout Rooster, raging at the dawn
Wakes us so early?

A warrior-king is on fire!
His armour is all crooked daggers and scimitars
And it's shivering red-hot – with rage!

And he screams out through his megaphone:
'Give me back my Queens!'

What's happened?

He fell asleep, a King of Tropic India
With ten thousand concubines, each one
Gorgeous as a volcanic sunset –

But now he wakes, turned inside out – a rooster!
With eleven flea-bitten hens!

And he remembers it all. No wonder he screeches:
'Give me back my Queens!'

No wonder his scarlet cheeks vibrate like a trumpet!

TED HUGHES, UK

# The Pit

Where do the roots go?
  Look down under the leaves.
Who put the moss there?
  These stones have been here too long.
Who stunned the dirt into noise?
  Ask the mole, he knows.
I feel the slime of a wet nest.
  Beware Mother Mildew.
Nibble again, fish nerves.

THEODORE ROETHKE (1908–63), USA

# Have You Ever Seen?

Have you ever seen a sheet on a river bed?
Or a single hair from a hammer's head?
Has the foot of a mountain any toes?
And is there a pair of garden hose?

Does the needle ever wink its eye?
Why doesn't the wing of a building fly?
Can you tickle the ribs of a parasol?
Or open the trunk of a tree at all?

Are the teeth of a rake ever going to bite?
Have the hands of a clock any left or right?
Can the garden plot be deep and dark?
And what is the sound of the birch's bark?

ANON.

# *from* Song of Myself

A child said *What is the grass?* fetching it to me with full
    hands;
How could I answer the child? I do not know what it is
    any more than he.
I guess it must be the flag of my disposition, out of hopeful
    green stuff woven.

Or I guess it is the handkerchief of the Lord,
A scented gift and remembrancer designedly dropt,
Bearing the owner's name someway in the corners, that we
    may see and remark, and say *Whose?*

Or I guess the grass is itself a child, the produced babe of
    the vegetation.

WALT WHITMAN (1819–92), USA

# What Is Pink?

What is pink? a rose is pink
By a fountain's brink.
What is red? a poppy's red
In its barley bed.
What is blue? the sky is blue
Where the clouds float thro'.
What is white? a swan is white
Sailing in the light.
What is yellow? pears are yellow,
Rich and ripe and mellow.
What is green? the grass is green,
With small flowers between.
What is violet? clouds are violet
In the summer twilight.
What is orange? why, an orange,
Just an orange!

CHRISTINA ROSSETTI (1830–94), UK

# Yellow

*Think of something yellow.*

The sun?
A fat ripe pear
or buttercup petals?

Yellow is butter.
Yellow is custard.
Yellow is yolks.

Yellow has all the answers.
Yellow is like
an advert that twists your eyes
till they light on yellow.

*What is yellow?*

Nobody answered.
Shakeela smiled
and stroked her yellow
shalwar khameez
so butterly
and buttercuply
that all our fingers turned yellow.

HELEN DUNMORE, UK

# O purple finch

'o purple finch
                please tell me why
this summer world (and you and i
who love so much to live)
                   must die'

'if i
    should tell you anything'
(that eagerly sweet carolling
self answers me)
                 'i could not sing'

e.e. cummings (1894–1962), USA

# Tell Me Why?

Daddy will you tell me why
There are no battleships in the sky?
   The reason is apparently
   They only battle on the sea

Then will you tell me if you please
Why grandfather clocks cannot sneeze?
   The reason is, or so I'm told
   They're too stupid and too old

Will you explain once and for all
Why little Jack Horner fell off the wall?
   It wasn't him it was little Bo Peep
   Now be a good boy and go to sleep

Daddy will you tell me when
Little boys grow into men?
   Some never do that's why they fight
   Now kiss me, let me hold you tight

For in the morning I must go
To join my regiment and so
   For Queen and country bravely die
   Son, oh son, please tell me why?

ROGER MCGOUGH, UK

# Boy on a Swing

Slowly he moves
to and fro, to and fro,
then faster and faster
he swishes up and down.

His blue shirt
billows in the breeze
like a tattered kite.

The world whirls by:
east becomes west,
north turns to south;
the four cardinal points
meet in his head.

      Mother!
Where did I come from?
When will I wear long trousers?
Why was my father jailed?

OSWALD MBUYISENI MTSHALI, Azania (South Africa)

# Where Are You, Mama?

Are you here, Mama,
or are you asleep
in a valley of that
orange moon?

Do your cheeks shine?
Does your gold tooth sparkle
in a field
of white daisies?

I stand here in frayed pants.
Will my sister turn up
with needle and thread?

My gloves slip from my hands.
Must I wear them
even if they are only
black gauze?

Will you come, Mama,
on some cloudless day
and let me eat strawberries?
I will find a fork
somewhere.

NELLIE WONG, China/USA

# The First Grief

'Oh! call my brother back to me,
   I cannot play alone;
The summer comes with flower and bee –
   Where is my brother gone?

'The butterfly is glancing bright
   Across the sunbeam's track;
I care not now to chase its flight –
   Oh! call my brother back.

'The flowers run wild – the flowers we sowed
   Around our garden tree;
Our vine is drooping with its load –
   Oh! call him back to me.

'He would not hear my voice, fair child!
   He may not come to thee;
The face that once like spring-time smiled
   On earth no more thou'lt see.

'A rose's brief, bright light of joy.
   Such unto him was given;
Go – thou must play alone, my boy –
   Thy brother is in heaven!'

'And has he left the birds and flowers,
    And must I call in vain;
And through the long, long summer hours,
    Will he not come again?

'And by the brook, and in the glade,
    Are all our wanderings o'er?
Oh! while my brother with me played,
    Would I had loved him more!'

FELICIA HEMANS (1793–1835), UK

# What Is Man's Body?

What is man's body? It is a spark from the fire
It meets water and it is put out.
What is man's body? It is a bit of straw
It meets fire and it is burnt.
What is man's body? It is a bubble of water
Broken by the wind.

Traditional: Gonds of India
from *Folksong of the Maikal Hills*
version by V. Elwin and S. Hivale

# Nothing Will Die

When will the stream be aweary of flowing
    Under my eye?
When will the wind be aweary of blowing
    Over the sky?
When will the clouds be aweary of fleeting?
When will the heart be aweary of beating?
    And nature die?
Never, oh! never, nothing will die;
  The stream flows,
  The wind blows,
  The cloud fleets,
  The heart beats,
    Nothing will die.

Nothing will die;
All things will change
Thro' eternity.
'Tis the world's winter;
Autumn and summer
Are gone long ago;
Earth is dry to the centre,
But spring, a new comer,
A spring rich and strange,
Shall make the winds blow
Round and round,

Thro' and thro',
  Here and there,
  Till the air
And the ground
Shall be fill'd with life anew.

The world was never made;
It will change, but it will not fade.
So let the wind range;
For even and morn
  Ever will be
  Thro' eternity.
Nothing was born;
Nothing will die;
All things will change.

ALFRED TENNYSON (1809–92), UK

# As Fit as a Fiddle

Grandfather George is as fit as a fiddle,
As fit as a fiddle right up from his middle,
Grandfather George is as fit as a fiddle,
As fit as a fiddle right down to his toes.

Grandfather George, whenever I meet him
Nips my right ear and asks me a riddle,
And when Mother questions him how he is keeping,
He slaps his left leg and says 'Fit as a fiddle!'

Once I said 'Grandfather George, why a fiddle,
Why is a fiddle especially fit?'
He laughed very loud and said 'Hey diddle-diddle,
I'll give you a sixpence if you'll answer that!'

So now I ask everyone, friends and relations,
People I talk to wherever I go,
I ask them on buses, in ships and at stations:
I suppose, by the way, that you do not know?

PAULINE CLARKE, UK

# All I Did Was Ask My Sister a Question

Why is water wet? Let's see –
Because . . . Well, silly, it has to be!
How could you drink it if it were dry?
If you got a drop of it in your eye
It would sting like sand and make you cry.
When it started to rain, it would come down dust.
You'd have to hold your breath till you bust
Or turn to powder inside your chest.
And how would I pass my swimming test
And get my badge? Not that you'd care.
You'd still be standing around somewhere
Asking foolish questions to get me mad!
Well, I'll tell Mother and she'll tell Dad.
Then see what he does to you for that!
And see if I care, you little brat!

JOHN CIARDI (1916–86), USA

# How Can I?

How can I wind up my brother
when I haven't got the key?

How can I turn on my charm
when I can't even find the switch?

How can I snap at my mother
when I'm not a crocodile?

How can I stir up my sister
when I'm not even holding a spoon?

How can I pick up my feet
and not fall to the ground on my knees?

How can I stretch my legs
when they're long enough already?

Parents! – They ask the impossible!

BRIAN MOSES, UK

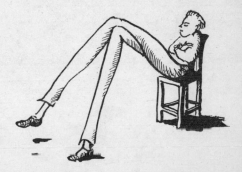

# Why?

Why are the leaves always green, Dad?
Why are there thorns on a rose?
Why do you want my neck clean, Dad?
Why do hairs grow from your nose?

Why can dogs hear what we can't, Dad?
Why has the engine just stalled?
Why are you rude about Aunt, Dad?
Why are you going all bald?

Why is Mum taller than you, Dad?
Why can't the dog stand the cat?
Why's Grandma got a moustache, Dad?
Why are you growing more fat?

Why don't you answer my questions?
You used to; you don't any more.
Why? Tell me why. Tell me why, Dad?
Do you think I am being a bore?

JOHN KITCHING, UK

# Questions of a Studious Working Man

Who built Thebes of the seven gates?
In the books you find the names of kings.
Was it the kings who hauled chunks of rock to the place?
And Babylon, many times demolished,
Who raised it up again so many times? In what houses
Of gold-glittering Lima did the builders live?
Where, the evening that the Great Wall of China was
    finished,
Did the masons go? Great Rome
Is full of triumphal arches. Over whom
Did the Caesars triumph? Had Byzantium, much praised
    in song,
Only palaces for its inhabitants? Even in fabulous
    Atlantis,

The very night the ocean engulfed it,
The drowning still roared for their slaves.
Young Alexander conquered India.
Was it he alone?
Caesar defeated the Gauls.
Did he not have a cook at least in his service?
Philip of Spain wept when his armada
Had sunk. Was he the only one to weep?
Frederick the Second won the Seven Years' War. Who
Else won that war?

Every page a victory.
Who cooked the feast for the victors?
Every ten years a great man.
Who paid the bill?

So many accounts
So many questions.

BERTOLT BRECHT (1898–1956), Germany
translated by Yvonne Kapp

## Wise One

Wise one, wise one
how long is a piece of string?

Twice as long as half its length.

Wise one, wise one
how do you kill a snake?

Put its tail in its mouth
and it'll eat itself up.

Wise one, wise one
What's at the end of a cat's tail?

A cat.

Wise one, wise one
How can I get a chick out of a boiled egg?

Feed it to the chicken
so it can lay it again.

Wise one, wise one
Why do bricklayers put mortar on bricks?

To keep the bricks together
and to keep the bricks apart.

Wise one, wise one
My parrot talks too much.

Give it a good book to read.

MICHAEL ROSEN, UK

# Will there really be a 'Morning'?

Will there really be a 'Morning'?
Is there such a thing as 'Day'?
Could I see it from the mountains
If I were as tall as they?

Has it feet like Water lilies?
Has it feathers like a Bird?
Is it brought from famous countries
Of which I have never heard?

Oh, some Scholar! Oh, some Sailor!
Oh, some Wise Man from the skies!
Please to tell a little Pilgrim
Where the place called 'Morning' lies!

EMILY DICKINSON (1830–86), USA

# You ask me

You ask me: 'How are you?'
        How can I know it?
'From where? Which family?'
        How can I know it?
You ask me: 'You are drunk,
        intoxicated –
From which sweet, heavy wine?'
        How can I know it?
If I myself am you,
        Well, who are you, then?
Are you this, are you that?
        How can I know it?

Rumi: 13th-century Persian mystic
translated by Reynold A. Nicholson

# Isn't My Name Magical?

Nobody can see my name on me.
My name is inside
and all over me, unseen
like other people also keep it.
   Isn't my name magic?

My name is mine only.
It tells I am individual,
the only special person it shakes
when I'm wanted.

If I'm with hundreds of people
and my name gets called,
my sound switches me on to answer
like it was my human electricity.
   Isn't that magical?

My name echoes across playground,
it comes, it demands my attention.
I have to find out who calls,
who wants me for what.
My name get blurted out in class,
it is a terror, at a bad time,
because somebody is cross.

My name gets called in a whisper
I am happy, because
my name may have touched me
with a loving voice.
    Isn't it all magic?

JAMES BERRY, Jamaica/UK

# The Dunce

Why does he still keep ticking?
  Why does his round white face
Stare at me over the books and ink,
  And mock at my disgrace?
Why does that thrush call, 'Dunce, dunce, dunce!'?
  Why does that bluebottle buzz?
Why does the sun so silent shine? –
  And what do I care if it does?

WALTER DE LA MARE (1873–1956), UK

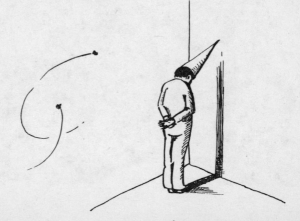

# What Is One?

One is the sun,
a rhino's horn;
a drop of dew,
a lizard's tongue.

One is the world,
a lonely whale;
an elephant's trunk,
a monkey's tail.

One is an acorn,
one is a moon;
one is a forest,
felled too soon.

JUDITH NICHOLLS, UK

# The Man in the Wilderness

The Man in the Wilderness asked of me
'How many blackberries grow in the sea?'
I answered him as I thought good,
'As many red herrings as grow in the wood.'

The Man in the Wilderness asked me why
His hen could swim, and his pig could fly.
I answered him briskly as I thought best,
'Because they were born in a cuckoo's nest.'

The Man in the Wilderness asked me to tell
The sands in the sea and I counted them well.
Says he with a grin, 'And not one more?'
I answered him bravely, 'You go and make sure!'

ANON.

# What Do Teachers Dream Of?

What do teachers dream of,
In mountains and in lowlands?
They dream of exclamation marks,
Full stops and semi-colons!

COLIN WEST, UK

# A Small Discovery

Father,
Where do giants go to cry?

To the hills
Behind the thunder?
Or to the waterfall?
I wonder.

(Giants cry.
I know they do.
Do they wait
Till nighttime too?)

JAMES A. EMANUEL, African-American

# Clowns

Where do clowns go,
what do clowns eat,
where do clowns sleep,

what do clowns do,
when nobody,
just nobody laughs
any more,
Mummy?

MIROSLAV HOLUB, Czechoslovakia
translated by Jar Mila and Ian Milner

# The Hangman at Home

What does the hangman think about
When he goes home at night from work?
When he sits down with his wife and
Children for a cup of coffee and a
Plate of ham and eggs, do they ask
Him if it was a good day's work
And everything went well or do they
Stay off some topics and talk about
The weather, baseball, politics
And the comic strips in the papers
And the movies? Do they look at his
Hands when he reaches for the coffee
Or the ham and eggs? If the little
Ones say, Daddy, play horse, here's
A rope – does he answer like a joke:
I seen enough rope for today?
Or does his face light up like a
Bonfire of joy and does he say:
It's a good and dandy world we live
In. And if a white face moon looks
In through a window where a baby girl
Sleeps and the moon-gleams mix with
Baby ears and baby hair – the hangman –
How does he act then? It must be easy
For him. Anything is easy for a hangman,
I guess.

CARL SANDBURG (1878–1967), USA

63

# Mirror Poem

If I look within the mirror,
Deep inside its frozen tears,
Shall I see the man I'll marry
Standing at my shoulder,
   Leaning down the years?

Shall I smile upon the mirror,
Shall my love look, smiling, back?
Midnight on Midsummer's eve:
What becomes of marriage
   If the glass should crack?

KIT WRIGHT, UK

# How can I describe

How can I describe
what is love
and when it is born
and where it is seen
and who found it
and how?

A connoisseur
draws out love
with tender care
from the pulsation of leaves,
from the rays of the flowers . . .

from Love Songs of Chandidas (15th century), Bengal
translated by Deben Bhattacharya

# Answer to a Child's Question

Do you ask what the birds say? The Sparrow, the Dove,
The Linnet and Thrush say, 'I love and I love!'
In the winter they're silent – the wind is so strong;
What it says, I don't know, but it sings a loud song.
But green leaves, and blossoms, and sunny warm weather,
And singing, and loving – all come back together.
But the Lark is so brimful of gladness and love,
The green fields below him, the blue sky above,
That he sings, and he sings; and for ever sings he –
'I love my Love, and my Love loves me!'

SAMUEL TAYLOR COLERIDGE (1772–1834), UK

# Intelligence Test

'What do you use your eyes for?'
The white-coated man inquired.
'I use my eyes for looking,'
Said Toby, '– unless I'm tired.'

'I see. And then you close them,'
Observed the white-coated man.
'Well done. A very good answer.
Let's try another one.

'What is your nose designed for?
What use is the thing to you?'
'I use my nose for smelling,'
Said Toby, 'Don't you, too?'

'I do indeed,' said the expert,
'That's what the thing is for.
Now I've another question to ask you,
Then there won't be any more.

'What are your ears intended for?
Those things at each side of your head?
Come on – don't be shy – I'm sure you can say.'
'For washing behind,' Toby said.

VERNON SCANNELL, UK

# Why Do You Write Poems?

Because my stomach is empty,
Because my throat's itching,
Because my bellybutton's laughing
Because my heart is love burning.

NANAO SAKAKI, Japan

# Where Does Laughter Begin?

Does it start in your head
and spread to your toe?

Does it start in your cheeks
and grow downwards so
till your knees feel weak?

Does it start with a tickle
in your tummy so
till you want to jump right out

of all your skin?
Or does laughter simply begin

with your mouth?

JOHN AGARD, Guyana/UK

## *from* The Merchant of Venice

Tell me where is fancy bred,
Or in the heart or in the head?
How begot, how nourished?
   Reply, reply.
It is engender'd in the eyes,
With gazing fed; and fancy dies
In the cradle where it lies.
   Let us all ring fancy's knell;
   I'll begin it, – Ding, dong, bell.
Ding, dong, bell.

WILLIAM SHAKESPEARE (1564–1616), UK

# Nursery Rhyme

What do we use to wash our hair?
We use shampoo to wash our hair.
It's tested scientifically for damage to the eyes
by scientists who, in such matters, are acknowledged to be
	wise.
Shampoo. Wash hair. Nice, clean habit.
Go to sleep now, darling.
It doesn't hurt the rabbit.

What makes lather in the bath tub?
Soap makes lather in the bath tub.
Rub-a-dub till bubbles bob along the rubber ducks race!
But don't get any in your mouth because soap has a nasty
	taste.
Bath time. Slippy soap! Can't quite grab it!
Let's get dried now, darling.
It doesn't hurt the rabbit.

What makes us better when we're ill?
Medicine helps us when we're ill.
Years of research helped to develop every pill you take,
Like that one we gave you when you had a tummy ache.
Cut knee. Antiseptic. Gently dab it.

Kiss you better, darling.
It doesn't hurt the rabbit.
It doesn't hurt
It doesn't hurt
It doesn't hurt the rabbit.

CAROL ANN DUFFY, UK

## Why Do People Need

Why do people need a head?
That is where the rot starts.

Why do people need a language?
The bird is caught because of its own singing.

Why do people need a nose?
They cannot smell their own stupidity.

Why do people need a heart?
It beats and beats then suddenly stops.

JON MILOS, Romania/Serbo-Croatia
translated by Brenda Walker

# Questions I Couldn't Answer When Asked by My Four-year-old Nephew . . .

  i  Why doesn't the river flow sidewise
      – bank to bank – ?

 ii  If 1 plus 1 is 2
      & two plus two makes 4

      how come 0 plus 0 is always zero?

iii  What do the eyes of a bubble see?

iv  little daisies
     little lotuses
     little arches of rainbows
     &
     little birds
     little animals
     little oceans
     &
     little mountains
     &
     little people
     why didn't god make the world that way?

 v  Who is lonelier – the sun or the moon?

vi  If all of us talked in songs
     & not in words

     would we still be fighting?

vii  Why must everything die, Badbaba?

DEBA PATNAIK, India

75

# The world is not to blame

The world is not to blame;
Therefore why blame the world?

Blame should fall on my head
And those like me. A glass

Holds wine; where does blame lie;
The man who presses the grape

Or he who drinks the wine?

ABU'L-'ALA AL-MA'ARRI (973–1057), Syria
translated by G. B. H. Wightman and A. Y. al-Udhari

# Ecclesiasticus

Who can number the sand of the sea,
And the drops of rain,
And the days of eternity?
Who can find out the height of heaven,
And the breadth of the earth,
And the deep, and wisdom?
Wisdom hath been created before all things,
And the understanding of prudence from everlasting.
The word of God most high is the fountain of
    wisdom;
And her ways are everlasting commandments.

Authorized King James Version

# Days

What are days for?
Days are where we live.
They come, they wake us
Time and time over.
They are to be happy in:
Where can we live but days?

Ah, solving that question
Brings the priest and the doctor
In their long coats
Running over the fields.

PHILIP LARKIN (1922–85), UK

# Question

What's today?
A Monday?
But Monday was
last week.

Tuesday?
But it was Tuesday all last year,
nothing but Tuesday.

Wednesday?
The century before this one, as far as I know,
fell on a Wednesday.

Thursday?
On a Thursday
Carthage was sacked,
on a Thursday
the Library in Alexandria burned.
Don't tell me that since then
not one day has passed.

Friday? Saturday?
Yes I've heard
of those days.
No fairy tales, please.

Sunday perhaps?
The time before the Creation
was called Sunday.
I remember that.

You see, all the days of the week *have been*.
For us there's no new one
left.

MARIN SORESCU, Romania
translated by Michael Hamburger

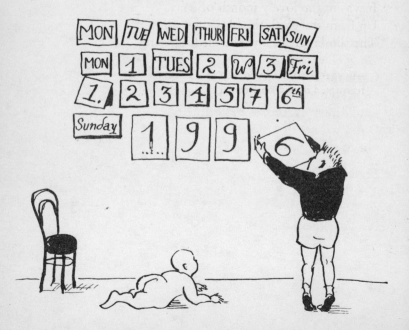

# Tell Me by Whom the Clock Was Planned

Tell me by whom the clock was planned:
The second hand, and the minute hand?
There was a sad man, cold as stone.
He sat on a Winter's night, alone,
And counted the secret squeaks of the mouse,
The woodworm's peckings upon the house.

Tell me who first invented the kiss?
That was a mouth on fire with bliss.
He kissed, unthinking, all through the day.
It was in the lovely month of May.
Up from the earth the blossoms sprang,
The sun laughed, and the birds all sang.

HEINRICH HEINE (1797–1856), Germany
translated by Aaron Kramer

# What's the weather on about?

What's the weather on about?
Why is the rain so down on us?
Why does the sun glare at us so?

Why does the hail dance so prettily?
Why is the snow such an overall?
Why is the wind such a tearaway?

Why is the mud so fond of our feet?
Why is the ice so keen to upset us?
Who does the weather think it is?

GAVIN EWART, UK

# Answer July

Answer July –
Where is the Bee –
Where is the Blush –
Where is the Hay?

Ah, said July –
Where is the Seed –
Where is the Bud –
Where is the May –
Answer Thee – Me –

Nay – said the May –
Show me the Snow –
Show me the Bells –
Show me the Jay!

Quibbled the Jay –
Where be the Maize –
Where be the Haze –
Where be the Bur?
Here – said the Year –

EMILY DICKINSON (1830–86), USA

# Who knows if the moon's

who knows if the moon's
a balloon, coming out of a keen city
in the sky – filled with pretty people?
(and if you and i should

get into it, if they
should take me and take you into their balloon,
why then
we'd go up higher with all the pretty people

than houses and steeples and clouds:
go sailing
away and away sailing into a keen
city which nobody's ever visited, where

always
        it's
            Spring) and everyone's
in love and flowers pick themselves

e.e. cummings (1894–1962), USA

84

# Eclipse of the Moon

Whose shadow's that?

Who walked in the evening
at his own ghost's back?

Who trod in the circle,
left a toe-print on the frozen pond?

Who looked in the mirror
and clouded the glass?

Who snatched the white moth
in his closed fist?

Who drowned
reaching for the coin?

GILLIAN CLARKE, UK

# Harlem (What happens to a Dream Deferred?)

What happens to a dream deferred?

Does it dry up
like a raisin in the sun?
Or fester like a sore –
And then run?
Does it stink like rotten meat?
Or crust and sugar over –
like a syrupy sweet?

Maybe it just sags
like a heavy load.

*Or does it explode*?

LANGSTON HUGHES (1902–67), African-American

# How Many, How Much

How many slams in an old screen door?
  Depends how loud you shut it.
How many slices in a bread?
  Depends how thin you cut it.
How much good inside a day?
  Depends how good you live 'em.
How much love inside a friend?
  Depends how much you give 'em.

SHEL SILVERSTEIN, USA

# Illness

(Written when he was paralysed)

Dear friends, there is no cause for so much sympathy.
I shall certainly manage from time to time to take my
    walks abroad.
All that matters is an active mind, what is the use of feet?
By land one can ride in a carrying-chair; by water, be
    rowed in a boat.

PO CHU-I, 9th-century China
translated by Arthur Waley

88

## *from* The Bed Book

You can take out your Bed
Shrunk small as a pea
And water it till
It grows suitably.

Yes, a Pocket-size Bed
Works very well
Only how can you tell,
O how can you tell

It won't shrink back
To the size of a pea
While you're asleep in it?
*Then* where would you be!

SYLVIA PLATH (1932–63), USA

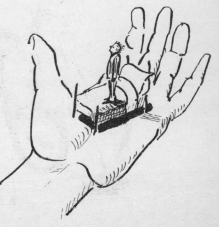

89

# Cœur Simple

Where is the sky hurrying to
Over my head,
Mother, is the sky hurrying
To bed?

Where is the sky hurrying to
Over my head?
Where it will be hurrying to
When you are dead.

STEVIE SMITH (1902–71), UK

# The Outsider

'Whom do you love the most, oh man of mystery? Tell me,
    is it your father, your mother, your sister, or your
    brother?'
  'I have neither father nor mother, neither sister nor
    brother.'
  'Your friends?'
  'You're using a word whose meaning has to this day
    eluded me.'
  'Your country?'
  'I do not know in what latitude it lies.'
  'Beauty?'
  'Beauty I would love with all my heart, were she a
    goddess and immortal.'
  'Money?'
  'I hate it as you hate God.'
  'Well what do you love then, extraordinary outsider?'
  'I love the clouds . . . the clouds that pass by . . . over
    there . . . over there . . . the marvellous clouds!'

CHARLES BAUDELAIRE (1821–67), France
translated by Rosemary Lloyd

# Index of Poets

# Index of First Lines

# Acknowledgements

We would like to thank the following authors, publishers and
agents for their kind permission to use work by:

JOHN AGARD: 'How Laughter Helped Stop the Argument' and
'Where Does Laughter Begin?' from *Laughter is an Egg* (Puffin,
1994). CHARLES BAUDELAIRE: 'The Outsider' from *Prose
Poems*, translated by Rosemary Lloyd, World's Classics Series
(Oxford, 1991), © Rosemary Lloyd, by permission of Oxford
University Press. JAMES BERRY: 'Isn't My Name Magical?' from
*Isn't My Name Magical?* (Longman), by permission of the
Longman Group Limited. SUBRAMANYA BHARATI: 'A New
Hymn to the Sun' from *The Elek Book of Oriental Verse*, edited
by Keith Bosley (Paul Elek Publishing, 1979). CHARLES
CAUSLEY: 'Morwenstow' from *Collected Poems* (Macmillan), by
permission of David Higham Associates. JOHN CIARDI: 'All I
Did Was Ask My Sister a Question' from *Doodle Soup* by John
Ciardi. Text copyright © 1985 by Myra J. Ciardi. Reprinted by
permission of Houghton Mifflin Co. All rights reserved. ROBERT
CLAIRMOUNT: 'The Answers' from *The Golden Treasury of
Poetry*, edited by Louis Untermeyer (Collins). GILLIAN CLARKE:
'Eclipse of the Moon' from *Selected Poems* by permission of
Carcanet Press Ltd. E. E. CUMMINGS: 'Who knows if the
moon's' reprinted from *Complete Poems 1904–1962*, edited by
George J. Firmage, by permission of W. W. Norton & Company
Ltd. © 1925, 1976, 1991 by the Trustees for the e. e. cummings
Trust and George James Firmage. 'O purple finch' reprinted from
*Complete Poems 1904–1962*, edited by George J. Firmage, by
permission of W. W. Norton & Company Ltd. © 1963, 1991 by
the Trustees for the e. e. cummings Trust. WALTER DE LA MARE:
'The Dunce' from *The Complete Poems of Walter de la Mare*,

Books Ltd. SPIKE MILLIGAN: 'Questions, Quistions & Quoshtions' © Spike Milligan, by permission of Spike Milligan Productions Ltd. JON MILOS: 'Bulls and Snails' and 'Why do People Need?' from *Through the Needle's Eye* (Forest Books, 1990), translated by Brenda Walker, © Brenda Walker. BRIAN MOSES: 'How Can I?' © Brian Moses, from *Rice, Pie and Moses* published by Macmillan Children's Books. OSWALD MBUYISENI MTSHALI: 'Boy on a Swing' © OSWALD MBUYISENI MTSHALI, 1971. Reprinted from *Sounds of a Cowhide Drum* (1971), by permission of Oxford University Press. JUDITH NICHOLLS: 'What is One?' © Judith Nicholls, 1994. Reprinted from *Storm's Eye* (1994) by permission of Oxford University Press. MERVYN PEAKE: 'How Fly the Birds of Heaven' by permission of David Higham Associates. SYLVIA PLATH: from *The Bed Book* by permission of Faber and Faber Ltd. THEODORE ROETHKE: 'The Pit' from the *Collected Poems of Theodore Roethke*, by permission of Faber and Faber Ltd. MICHAEL ROSEN: 'Wise One' from *Quick, Let's Get Out of Here* (André Deutsch Ltd) by permission of Scholastic Publications Ltd. RUMI: 'You ask me' from *I am Wind You Are Fire: The Life and Word of Rumi* by Annmarie Schimel, © 1992. Reprinted by arrangement with Shambhala Publications, Inc., 300 Massachusetts Avenue, Boston, MA 02115. CARL SANDBURG: 'The Hangman at Home' from *Smoke and Steel* by Carl Sandburg, © 1920 by Harcourt Brace & Company and renewed 1948 by Carl Sandburg. Reprinted by permission of the publisher. VERNON SCANNELL: 'Intelligence Test' copyright Vernon Scannell, by permission of the author. STEVE SMITH: 'Coeur Simple' from *The Collected Poems of Stevie Smith* (Penguin Twentieth-Century Classics) by permission of James MacGibbon. MARTIN SORESCU: 'Question' from *Selected Poems*, by permission of Bloodaxe Books. BRIAN SWANN: 'Who Will Stop the Sun?' an adaptation of a Native

American poem by permission of Brian Swann. COLIN WEST: 'What Do Teachers Dream Of?' by permission of the author. KIT WRIGHT: 'Mirror Poem' from *Cat Among the Pigeons* by permission of Penguin Books Ltd.

Faber and Faber Limited apologize for any errors or omissions in the above list and would be grateful to be notified of any corrections that should be incorporated in the next edition or reprint of this volume.